GROWING UP KIND

BY ROSE ANGEBRANDT

Published and written by Rose Angebrandt

ISBN: 978-1-9991187-6-1

Copyright © 2020 by Rose Angebrandt

www.roseangebrandt.com

For Keigan and Ayzlin

You are loved more than words can say

I'm Breanna. I want to grow up to be a kind person.

*What can **I** do to be kind?*

I see people being kind every day. Kindness makes people feel **special**! I can be kind by what I say and what I do.

Let me see...

Kindness can be a smile. Smiles make everyone feel **happy** and feeling happy makes everyone **smile**!

I think **smiling at someone** is being kind. Do you have a BIG happy smile to share?

I can help Mommy make breakfast. I will surprise her with my **special** Cereal and Milk. Mommy will like that.

*I think **surprise helping** is being kind. What surprise things can you do to help at home?*

I can read my **favorite** books to my Grandpa.
He doesn't see very good and I can be his
eyes when I read. Grandpa will like that.

*I think **reading** to my Grandpa is a
kind thing to do. Do you have favorite
books you can read to someone?*

Grandpa likes to tell me about when he was a little boy. I can listen to and **LOVE** all of his wonderful stories. Grandpa will like that.

*I think **listening** is being kind. Do you know what makes a good listener?*

I see Mrs. Baker on her porch when I walk to School. I can wish her a **SUPER-DUPER** beautiful day. Mrs. Baker will like that.

*I think **saying nice things** is being kind. What is a nice thing you can say to someone?*

My Teacher at School is Miss Lee. I can bring her Flowers to show I **really** like her! Miss Lee will like that.

I think **showing someone you like them** is being kind. What kind thing can you do for someone you like?

I can be the first to say **"Hi"** to new kids at School. They must be nervous. I want them to know they have a **friend**. New kids will like that.

*I think **being understanding** is being kind. Are you the first to say **"Hi"** to new friends?*

Mommy puts the most **yummy delicious** Chocolate Cookies in my Lunchbox. I can share my Cookies at Lunch. My friends will **love** them!

*I think **sharing** is being kind. Do you like to share things you love?*

Mrs. Theresa is the Lunchroom Lady at School. She has a **big** job cleaning up. I can help clean **messy** tables. Mrs. Theresa will like that.

*I think **helping to clean** is being kind.*

Do you like to help clean up?

The School Playground is fun. We play many fun games. I can play games that **all** of the kids play together! I **KNOW** the kids like that.

*I think **including everyone** is being kind. Do you play games that are fun for everyone?*

I can even **MAKE** things that are kind. I can draw, colour and cut out Hearts. I can give them to my family so they **ALWAYS** have my love with them. My family will like that.

*I think **showing love** is kind. How do you let your family know you love them?*

It is easy to be **kind**.

I can **smile** and make people happy.

I can **be helpful** at home and School.

I can **read and listen** to wonderful stories.

I can **say nice things** and feel good inside.

I can **give** flowers to show someone I like them.

I can **make new friends** and play lots
of games with **everybody**!

EVERYONE *will like that!*

I **can** and *will* do as many *kind things* every day as I can. I **WILL** grow up to be a *very* **KIND** person! **and...** Do you know what?...

I *will like that!*

Have a **KIND** *day!*

Hello Readers! ... Leave a Review?

Amazon Reviews can make a huge difference
to the overall success of this Book.

If you enjoyed reading this Book as much as I have enjoyed
writing it, please take a few moments to leave a quick Review.

I would really appreciate it!

Thank YOU!

ROSE ANGEBRANDT

Made in the USA
Coppell, TX
11 December 2020